020120

W   Vogler

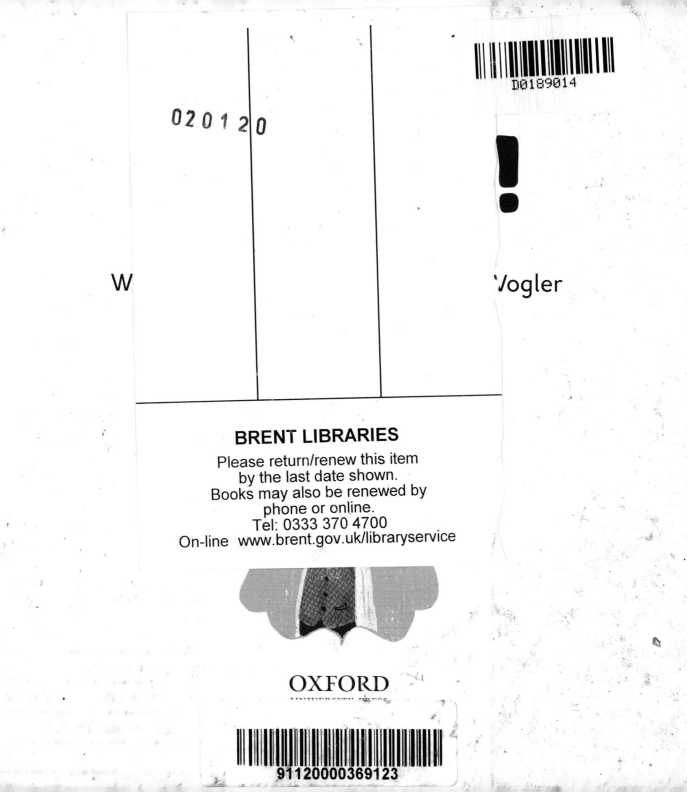

OXFORD

D0189014

91120000369123

There was a boy called Jack. Jack sat about the house all day.
"Oh, Jack! Get a job," said his mum.

Jack got a job at the baker's shop.

Mr Brown the baker gave him a penny
for his pay, but he lost it.

"Oh, Jack! I'm very cross with you," said his mum. "Put it in your pocket next time."

Jack got a job in the dairy.

Mrs Green the dairy owner gave him
a pot of milk for his pay.

On the way home he put it in his pocket.
The milk spilled onto the ground.

"Oh, Jack!" said his mum. "Put it on your head next time."

Jack got a job at the market.

Mr White the stallholder gave him
a cheese for his pay.

On the way home he put it on his head.
But the sun was very hot!
The cheese melted.

Jack got a job at the cake shop.

Mr Grey the shopkeeper gave him
a cake for his pay.

On the way home he put it on a lead.

"Oh, Jack! You don't think," said his mum.
"Carry it on your shoulder next time."

Jack got a job on
the farm.

Mrs Gold the farmer gave him a donkey
for his pay.

On the way home he carried it on his shoulder. Lots of people saw him and chuckled.

Jack came by a big house.
A girl sat at the window.
She was very rich, but very sad.

She looked and saw Jack with the
donkey on his shoulder.
The girl giggled and giggled.

Jack made her happy.
They got married and lived happily
ever after.

23

Once upon a time...

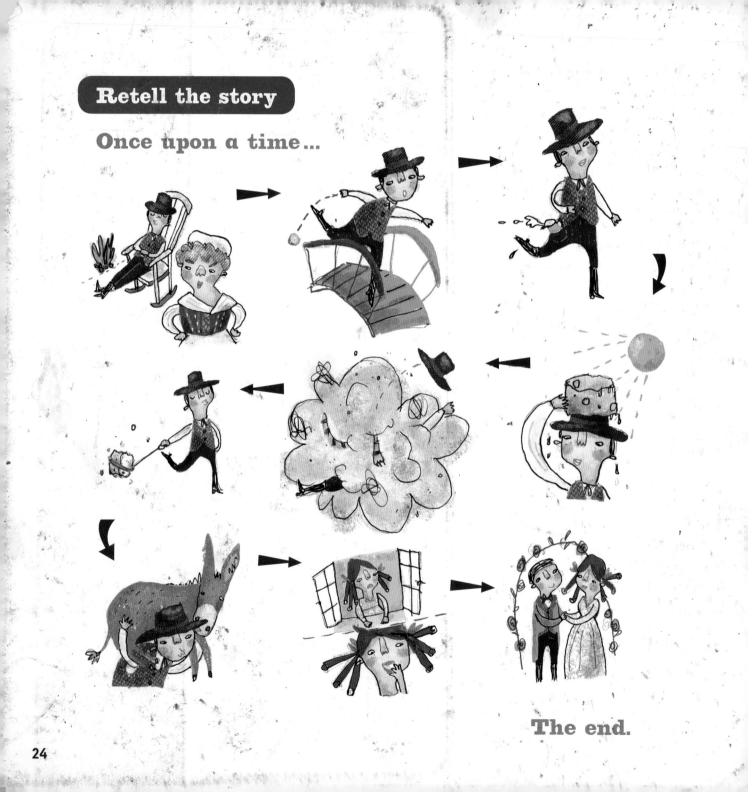

The end.

24